IMAGINE THAT™

Licensed exclusively to Imagine That Publishing Ltd
Tide Mill Way, Woodbridge, Suffolk, IP12 1AP, UK
www.imaginethat.com
Copyright © 2018 Imagine That Group Ltd
All rights reserved
0 2 4 6 8 9 7 5 3 1
Manufactured in China

Written by Dorothea DePrisco Wang
Illustrated by Claudine Gévry

ISBN 978-1-78700-859-5

A catalogue record for this book is available from the British Library

My Baby

Written by Dorothea DePrisco Wang
Illustrated by Claudine Gévry

Daddy Bear is proud and strong.

But he is also gentle.

He cuddles his baby with his large furry feet.

Mummy Giraffe is long-legged and fast.

But she is also kind.

She nudges her baby with her long soft neck.

Daddy Lion is
mighty and quick.

But he is also loving.

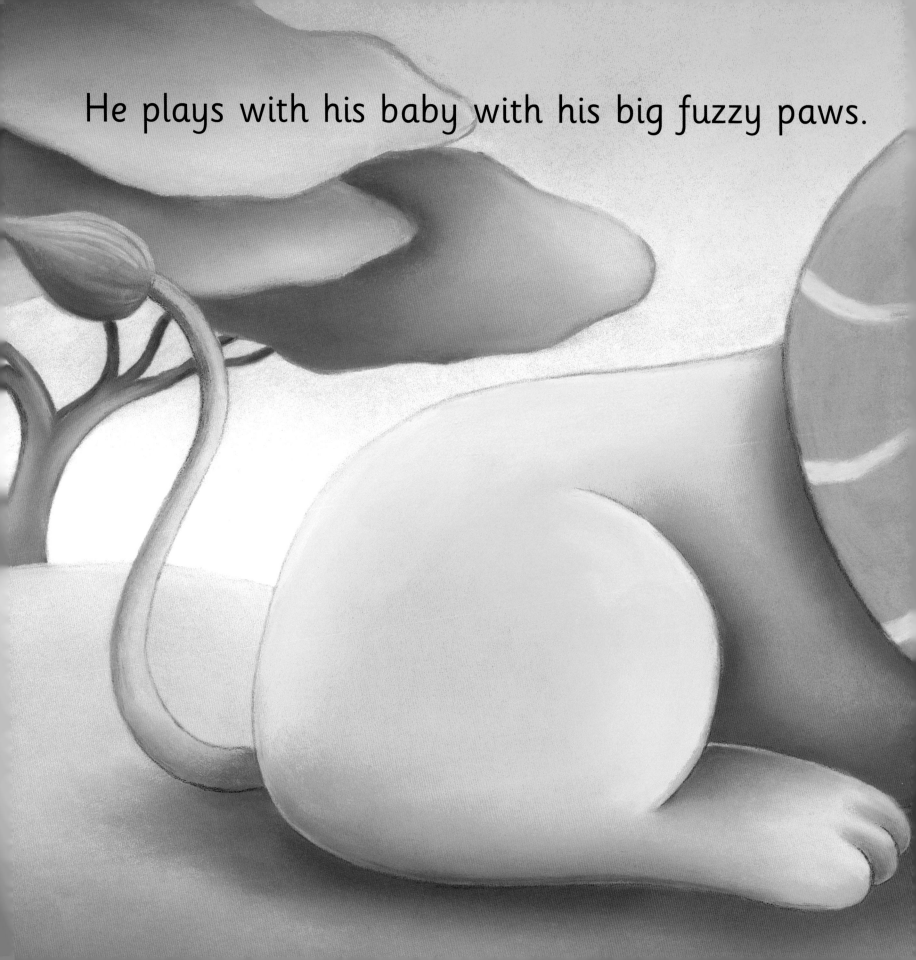

He plays with his baby with his big fuzzy paws.

Mummy Elephant is big and powerful.

But she is also tender.

She nuzzles her baby with her long warm trunk.

Animal babies,

no matter who they are ...

are loved by their parents ...

... near and far.

'I love you, little one.'